THE ANIMALS OF DOCTOR SCHWEITZER

Also by Jean Fritz

FISH HEAD

121 PUDDING STREET

THE LATE SPRING

THE CABIN FACED WEST

CHAMPION DOG PRINCE TOM
(with TOM CLUTE)

THE ANIMALS OF DOCTOR SCHWEITZER

by Jean Fritz

Illustrated by Douglas Howland

Coward-McCann, Inc.   New York

*Grateful acknowledgment is made here to
Madame Emmy Martin for her cooperation,
to Charles Joy, whose many books on Dr.
Schweitzer were the source of much of the
material here, to Erica Anderson for her
suggestions and for her warm interest.*

Library of Congress Catalog Card Number: 58-10189
Manufactured in the United States of America

To Alice Torrey

THE ANIMALS OF DOCTOR SCHWEITZER

ON the left-hand side of Africa, soon after the land humps into the ocean and begins wandering south, there is a wide yellow river called the Ogowe. In all the world there is no country wilder than the country this river runs through. Both sides of the river are lined with black jungles of trees, tangles of fern, and swamps of papyrus higher than a tall man's head. Palm trees lean over the river with snakes and monkey tails dangling from the branches like shadows on a line.

All the sounds of the Ogowe country are wild and fearful sounds – the trumpeting of elephants, the screams of panthers, the cries of gorillas, the stomping of buffalo. And the silences are wild and fearful too. A crocodile, pushing his eyes up over the edge of the water, is silent. A white-bellied shark, streaking up river, is as silent as a pointed knife. Up and down the Ogowe River there is wildness like the wildness when the world first began.

Except for one spot. In the middle of this wildness there is a clearing. Giant mahogany trees have been cut down and made into buildings. Lemon trees and grapefruit trees have been lined up neatly into orchards. At daybreak a rooster crows on the top of a barnyard fence; at night a piano plays among the palm trees. Lambs and cats and dogs and chickens and ducks and wild things that have wandered in from the jungle and been tamed are at home in a little patch of gentleness on the long Ogowe River. For here is Dr. Schweitzer, the Great Doctor, who has built a hospital in the center of a jungle, who has brought love to a land of fear.

He walks about the hospital grounds, and dogs and cats follow him. Pigs nudge him for attention; monkeys swoop down upon his shoulder. A pelican guards his bedroom door; an antelope sleeps in the room next to him. The Great Doctor takes a scrap of bread from his pocket and feeds it to a pet antelope. In another pocket there may be a bite for a hungry owl. All of these animals have their names and their stories; they are the friends of the Great Doctor.

One of his best friends is Monsieur le Pelican.

In the beginning, of course, Monsieur le Pelican was not Monsieur le Pelican at all. He had no name. He didn't know the Great Doctor nor dream that he would ever live any place except where he lived right now, among the feathery papyrus stalks on the riverbank. All he knew was the warm feeling of the sun on his white feathers. And the warm feeling of his mother's wings when he and the other two baby pelicans leaned close to her in the African night. And the wonderfully warm and comfortable feeling in his stomach after his mother opened her mouth and let him feed from the pouch attached to her bill. He was too little to know much about danger except that sometimes his mother wanted him to sit very still among the papyrus leaves. She wouldn't even allow him to ruffle a wing.

But one day even his mother didn't know that danger was near. She was standing at the edge of the water looking for foolish little minnows to scoop up into her pouch. She didn't hear the hunter slipping quietly around the bend of the river in his canoe. He dipped his paddle in and out of the water so smoothly, it didn't make a sound. In and out the paddle moved, as softly as a butterfly opening and closing its wings. When the mother pelican looked up, it was too late. The hunter raised his gun and shot. As he pulled his canoe up to the river bank, he saw the three baby pelicans. They were sitting among the papyrus leaves, still as the eggs they were hatched from. Their heads were pulled so far down into their bodies that their orange beaks seemed to stick straight out from their round little white stomachs.

Again the hunter raised his gun. Perhaps he was even pointing it at one of the white stomachs when the thought of the Great Doctor darted into his mind, swift and unexpected as a hummingbird. It was said that the Great Doctor up the river did not like baby birds and animals to be killed. He even

paid money if they were brought to him alive. This was queer but it was true. A man in the hunter's own village had once been given five francs for bringing in a baby antelope. The hunter smiled. He lowered his gun and picked up the three baby pelicans, placing them so that their webbed orange feet sat squarely on the bottom of the canoe. Then he turned and headed upstream.

When the hunter reached the hospital grounds, he may have been sorry for a moment that he had come. So many eyes watched him. Women washing clothes in the river stopped their washing and looked. Children gathered on the bank and stared.

"Do you bring a sick person?" they called.

The hunter shook his head. "Only three small pelicans," he said. "I wish to give them to the Great Doctor."

"This way, this way!" The children danced in front of the hunter. They led him through the courtyard, beneath the palm trees and parrots and black and yellow weaver birds.

Perhaps they found the Great Doctor among the houses where the sick people stay. Perhaps they found him outside helping to make new buildings. Perhaps he was seeing that the vegetable and fruit gardens were being cared for properly. He would be busy because he is always busy, but for a minute he stopped his work. He pushed his white pith helmet back a bit on his head and he smiled.

"Those are three fine pelicans," the doctor said. "You were right to bring them to me." He reached into his pocket and pulled out a little sock with some coins in it and handed a few coins to the hunter.

"*Akewa*," the hunter said. "Thank you."

The Great Doctor built a pen for the pelicans underneath the porch of his own house. Every day he brought fish from the hospital kitchen and placed them one at a time in the beak of each pelican. One little pelican was smaller and weaker than the other two. For this one the doctor saved an extra serving of fish and spoke an extra word of encouragement.

"Come, my friend," he would say, "eat and grow strong."

When the pelicans were a little bigger, the doctor decided it was time they had a lesson in catching their own food. He brought the fish from the kitchen as usual but he no longer placed it in their beaks.

"Now you are big enough to work for your

dinner," he said. He threw the fish into the air, at first close to their mouths so that it was easy for them to catch. Then he threw them farther away so the pelicans had to swing their beaks to catch the fish as they came down.

"Now, now," the doctor would laugh, "you two big ones have had enough. This is for your little brother."

The wings of the three pelicans grew wider and stronger. When they stretched them out now and flapped them at their sides, they made whirring noises in the air. Their beaks grew longer, their necks stretched up, and every day they wanted more and more fish.

"You're too big to live under a porch," the doctor told them, "and too hungry to feed from the kitchen. Come on out. Spread your wings and find the Ogowe River, where you can fish for yourselves."

Soon the three pelicans were going to the river every day. They would hide behind trees, watching for schools of minnows to swim by. Then they would swoop down, scoop them up, toss back their heads, and let the river water drool out on both sides of their long beaks as they swallowed their catch. But always one of the pelicans was slower than the other two. He stayed smaller and when the three went home in a line, he was always the last one. In the evening when the Great Doctor would meet the pelicans walking in the courtyard, he would stop and speak to the smallest one.

"And are you finding enough minnows in our river, my friend?" he might ask. He would reach into his pocket and perhaps he would find some special little tidbit for this smallest pelican.

One day went and the next day came on the long Ogowe River. Every day was very much the same for the three pelicans. Every morning the sun came up, setting the earth to steaming and the weaver birds to screeching in their basketlike nests. Then it was time to go to the river. Every evening at six o'clock the sun went down and the crickets and toads tuned up to sing. Then it was time to go home. But one day something very different happened. The three pelicans were at the water watching for minnows when all at once there was a great flapping in the air. A long, dark shadow fell across the river. The sky was filled with white wings and the air was filled with excitement. The season had come for the Big Flight when all the pelicans from inland waters flew toward the sea.

The three pelicans on the river bank saw the white wings and they felt the excitement. They stretched their own wings wider than they had ever stretched them before and they rose up into the sky, one behind the other, the smallest one last. Round and round the hospital grounds they circled and at last joined the long line of white wings disappearing over the rim of the earth. At the very end of the line the smallest pelican flapped his wings a few times and sailed, flapped his wings and sailed, just as the other pelicans did. But he didn't go far. Behind him and below him were the hospital grounds and the Great Doctor and the river and the courtyard all speckled with sunshine and noisy with weaver birds. The smallest pelican turned around, circled once more, and then dropped to the edge of the river. That night at six o'clock when the sun went down, the smallest pelican went back to the courtyard just as he had every evening, only this time he was alone.

When the Great Doctor saw him, his eyes crinkled with pleasure and his moustache turned

up at the corners with his smile. "Ah, my little friend," he said, "so you didn't go with your brothers. You decided to stay with me, did you?"

After the Big Flight, days went back to being the same for the smallest pelican except that he was no longer, of course, the smallest pelican. He was the only pelican and he was growing bigger and bulkier and bossier all the time. He made his home now on the porch roof of the Great Doctor's house and he appointed himself night watchman for the Great Doctor. Today he is still night watchman. From six o'clock in the evening when he flies up from the river to six o'clock in the morning he guards the front door of the Great Doctor's house as carefully as if he were a policeman with a billy club. No one but the Great Doctor himself and one or two especially trusted members of the hospital dares to go through that door unless he wants to be rapped on the head with a hard pelican beak. It is difficult to remember that this was once the smallest pelican. Now he is an enormous bird and a very dignified gentleman. He is Monsieur le Pelican.

"*Bon soir*, Monsieur le Pelican," the Great

Doctor says every evening as he comes home and greets his friend.

Monsieur le Pelican says nothing but it is clear what he would like to say. "You see? I am on duty as usual. You can count on me until six o'clock tomorrow morning."

Now when it is the time of year for the Big Flight, Monsieur le Pelican doesn't even stretch his wings. No. This is his home, his river, even his fish. Surely that is what he must have been thinking the day he saw the fisherwoman pull up a fish from his river and drop it into the bottom of her canoe. She was sitting in her canoe not far from the shore, within the jagged shadows of the palm trees, in the very part of the river where his own minnows swam. Monsieur le Pelican felt just as he did when a stranger knocked on the doctor's door in the evening. He felt as if his feathers had been ruffled deep inside him where, of course, there were no feathers to ruffle. Whenever he felt like this, he had to do something about it. So Monsieur le Pelican spread his wings and down he swooped headfirst into the fisherwoman's boat. Straight as an arrow from the sun he dropped, and he had the fish in his mouth when WHAM! The fisherwoman picked up the paddle of her canoe and hit Monsieur le Pelican hard across a leg.

Later that day when the Great Doctor was working on the broken leg, he reminded Monsieur le Pelican that there were enough fish in the Ogowe River for many fishermen. "And now until your leg is mended," the Great Doctor went on, "I am afraid, Monsieur, that I must carry you back and forth to the river."

And he did. Every morning the Great Doctor picked up the big, white, feathery armful that was Monsieur le Pelican and together they walked under the palm trees to the yellow river. The sun, then, would be pushing itself, hot and round, up one side of the African world. In the evening when the sun was dropping behind the other side of the African world, the Great Doctor would carry his friend home again. And all the time between sunset and sunrise and between sunrise and sunset Monsieur le Pelican's leg was growing stronger.

Now, of course, his leg is well again and Monsieur le Pelican goes down alone to the river. When visitors and new patients arrive, he is the first one to greet them under the mango tree

where canoes dock. He lumbers up from behind a tree or rock and looks over each newcomer carefully. Day and night he must be on guard, he seems to say. Not only at the river bank and at the doctor's door; the whole hospital comes under his wing. Sometimes he follows the African sheep to pasture and, mounting an old stump, he stands guard while they graze. There is one big, horny ram who is his particular friend. He always stands close and pays special attention when Monsieur le Pelican starts lecturing from his stump. Surely this is what he is doing. He nods his head, flaps and points his wings, and becomes very excited. Perhaps he is warning the sheep against the dangers of the world outside. Perhaps, some people say, he is repeating one of the Great Doctor's own sermons.

"He is like Saint Francis," the Great Doctor says, "preaching to the animals." And he smiles, for the Great Doctor and Monsieur le Pelican are such good friends. Whenever the Great Doctor goes to Europe on a visit, he carries with him a picture of Monsieur le Pelican. No matter where he is, he puts the picture on his desk, and when he looks at it, he is glad.

There is another picture, too, that the Great Doctor carries with him. It is a picture of Leonie and Theodore, two antelope fawns who came to the hospital in much the same way that Monsieur le Pelican did. Walking in the jungle with their mother one day, these fawns fell into a deep pit dug by African hunters to trap animals. The mother was able to leap high to safety, but not the fawns. Their legs were spindly and unsteady. They were still at the bottom of the pit when the hunters came back.

"Only two babies," one hunter said. "Their mother has got away."

"Bad luck," the other hunter agreed but then, like the pelican hunter, he remembered the Great Doctor and his teaching. "We must not kill them," he said. "We'll take them to the Great Doctor. It is said that he has a special place in his heart for antelope."

When the hunters found the doctor, they could see at once that this was true. The Great Doctor looked at the little wobbling antelope, and his eyes grew tender. For a moment he felt as if all the heat and hard work of the day had been blown away by a fresh, cool breeze. What baby animal, he thought, is as lovely and lovable as the antelope fawn? He watched them balancing so delicately on their matchstick-thin legs, their ears pointed in alarm, their velvet eyes dark and round with fear.

"Do not be afraid, little ones," he said gently. "Everything will be all right."

The Great Dotor gave the hunters the usual reward and took the two antelope into his house, into his own bedroom. He closed the door.

"Here you will be safe," he said. "You see there are bars across the windows in case a stray leopard decides to pay a call. The noises of the jungle are far away. We shall share this bedroom together, you and I, shall we not? And at night we shall listen to the song of the crickets."

The Great Doctor built a pen for Leonie and Theodore next to his bedroom, and several times

a day fed them from a milk bottle. The fear that lay deep in the eyes of the antelope on their first day at the hospital soon melted away. Now they nuzzled the doctor for his attention. They pressed their shiny black noses against the cage when they heard his footsteps outide the door. Their tails trembled with excitement.

Every evening after supper the doctor let them out of their cage and for a while allowed them to play freely around his bedroom. "First," he said, "we must move anything that you could trip over. We must cover the pedals of the piano." The Great Doctor pulled a mat over the pedals, padding them carefully. "Now," he said, "it is safe. You may come out and play."

Sometimes when Leonie and Theodore tired of playing, they curled up at the Great Doctor's feet while he worked at his table with papers and pencil.

This is the time of day when most of the long row of the Great Doctor's books have been written. Sometimes it has been Sisi, the cat, who has kept him company while he works, falling asleep on his left hand while he goes on writing with his right. Then if anyone calls him, he says, "I cannot move. You can see Sisi is asleep." Sometimes it has been Tchu-Tchu or Caramba, his dogs, who have kept him company. Never has he been more happy, however, than when Leonie and Theodore were at his feet.

The trouble was that they were not always content to lie there quietly. Like all antelope, Leonie and Theodore soon discovered that they enjoyed chewing on anything that happened to be convenient. Sometimes it was the edge of the mat. Sometimes it was a leg of the Great Doctor's trousers. Once it was more important than either a mat or a trouser leg.

The Great Doctor wasn't looking and Leonie reached her lovely long neck up until her head rested on the edge of the doctor's table. There in front of her was a stack of crinkly, crumply papers. Very gently Leonie opened her mouth and she crinkled the papers and she crumpled them and she chewed them all up. She didn't know, of course, that she was eating a chapter of the Great Doctor's famous book, *The Philosophy of Civilization*.

When the Great Doctor discovered what had happened, he shook his head and he smiled. "Ah, Leonie," he said, "I see you have a taste for literature." And he wrote his chapter over again. After that he kept his work on a shelf too high for Leonie to reach and from time to time he brought Leonie a supply of manioc leaves to chew. Manioc leaves, the doctor told her, were just as crinkly, just as crumply as paper, and just as much fun to chew. Leonie agreed that this was so.

When Leonie and Theodore grew too big for their bedroom pen, the Great Doctor built them an enclosure under his porch. "But just because you are no longer in the bedroom," he said, "we shall not be cheated of our evenings together."

He made two collars—one for Leonie, one for Theodore. To each of them he attached a lead. Then one evening he went into their enclosure under the porch and he fastened the collars around their necks. "Now," he said, "together we shall go for a walk."

The Great Doctor led Leonie and Theodore out on their leashes. The three of them walked through the courtyard to a rock conveniently placed as a seat overlooking the Ogowe River. With his two antelope nosing into his hands, the doctor sat down on the rock and looked at the scene stretched out before him—the long yellow river, the noble pine trees, and the black forest beyond

rising like a wall on all sides. A crested crane rose from the water, trailing his thin legs like kite strings behind him. A kingfisher flashed up from the swamps. From the hospital courtyard came the faint barking of dogs and the end-of-day stirring of chickens. In the distant forest a tom-tom tapped and stopped and tapped again. The Doctor laid his hand on Leonie's head. "This is the peaceful time," he said. "We shall come back every evening and enjoy the twilight together. Is it agreed?"

Leonie nudged him gently. What a beautiful world it is from this hill, the doctor thought. Perhaps he thought of another hill where he played as a child—the gentler hillside which backed up to his boyhood home in Germany. Perhaps as he looked down at Leonie and Theodore, he was reminded of the prayer he used to say in that home. As a child, he could never understand why when he prayed with his mother, he should pray only for human beings. Every night after his mother had left the room, he closed his eyes again and added his own prayer for all living creatures.

"O Heavenly Father," he prayed, "protect and bless all things that have breath; guard them from all evil and let them sleep in peace."

Not all the doctor's friends have been as gentle and easy to manage as Leonie and Theodore. Thekla, a Red River hog, was one of his more mischievous pets. Time after time the Great Doctor had to shake his head. "Thekla, Thekla," he would sigh, "whatever am I to do with you?"

When Thekla first came to the hospital, she was a skinny, scrawny rust-colored piglet with a white stripe running down the middle of her back.

"We shall have to feed you up," the doctor said, "and give you a home." He tipped his head to one side and considered the sickly looking piglet. "Since we have given you the name that belongs to a famous lady in an opera story, I suppose you think you deserve a fancy house." The doctor nodded his head. "Perhaps you are right." And he set to work making Thekla a pen. When he had finished the fence, he took a shovel and started to dig inside. He made a nice, neat hollow space and then mixed some concrete. After a while he stood back and put his hands on his hips.

"There you are, my dear Thekla," he said, "you have a private swimming pool all your own."

All the people at the hospital came to admire Thekla's fine new home. After all, what other hog in the African jungle had a concrete swimming pool for her private splashing?

Thekla liked her home; there was no question about that because she always came back to it. But she was no homebody. In her opinion a home was to come back to, not to stay in. As soon as she was strong enough to dig a hole under her fence, she left home every morning, following a group of woodcutters who went to the forest to cut trees. Somewhere on the hospital grounds each day the doctor would call in a loud voice, "Now, to work!" If the woodcutters had not already left for the forest, they would leave then. And at their heels would be Thekla, romping back and forth, rooting and sniffling at all the smells of the jungle. In the evening there would be Thekla back again. She always came home with the woodcutters and trotted happily to her pen, letting herself in through the hole she had dug. Oh, she did like her pen at the end of the day and a swim after her romp in the woods!

Thekla always seemed to know when supper was over in the hospital dining room. More than anything else—more than her pen, more than her pool—this was what made it worth while to come home. For this was the time when the Great Doctor came to visit. Thekla would stand on her hind legs, her front legs resting on the fence, her nose pressed against it, and wait. Some evenings she might have to wait longer than others. The lanterns might be lit around the courtyard, but the doctor always came and in his pockets would always be the fruit peelings he had saved from the supper table. He would drop a piece of golden orange skin into Thekla's open snout. "And I suppose, my dear Thekla," he might smile, "you have been keeping house all day and waiting for me!"

If only Thekla had been happy just to go and come with the woodcutters! But one day, instead of going to the forest, she decided to explore the hospital grounds. She ran in the front door of one hospital building, clattered around for a while, and ran out again. She found another building and ran in and out of it. This was fun. She galloped under the beds of patients; she pushed between the legs of doctors and nurses. Oh, this was much more fun than a whole forest of woodcutters! No matter how many times Thekla was caught and taken back to her pen, she would break out and head straight for the hospital. Every day she found more and more exciting things to do. She stole food from the patients and raced away with it. She upset cooking pots and overturned furniture. She frightened children and she killed chickens. But always in the evening she would be back to her pen and wait for the Great Doctor, her front feet on the fence.

Even the doctor could do nothing with Thekla. The patients and the hospital staff chased and scolded and spanked Thekla, and filled up the holes under her fence, but it made no difference. As far as Thekla was concerned, home was still a place to come back to and not to stay in. Every day people at the hospital reported new trouble and on one

particularly bad day they threatened to kill Thekla.

That evening when the Great Doctor called on Thekla with his fruit peelings, he looked very sad. "Thekla," he said, "I am sorry that this is so, but in order to save your life we must send you away. Tomorrow you are going to the London Zoo. But wait and be patient and one day I shall come and visit you there."

The next day, while the Great Doctor stood under the mango tree at the canoe dock, Thekla was taken up the Ogowe River and shipped to London.

Three years later the Great Doctor went to London on important business. He had speeches to make and meetings to attend. People rushed him from one important place to another. At last the Great Doctor stopped all the hurrying and spoke to all the busy people. "I must have time," he said, "to go to the zoo. No matter how many important things there are to do, I must visit Thekla."

When Thekla saw the Great Doctor standing outside her cage, she galloped over to the fence. She put her front feet up and pressed her snout close, just as she always had.

"Ah, Thekla, Thekla," the Great Doctor said.

Then perhaps he pulled out of his pocket a fresh peeling of orange. Perhaps an apple peeling too.

After he had fed her, he looked around Thekla's new home. Yes, it was a fine, big home. She certainly couldn't dig her way out of this one but, perhaps, that didn't matter. Afer all, what hog in Africa had as grand a pen and as many admiring people coming to call every day?

Back at the hospital on the Ogowe River there have been other Red River hogs that have made their home with the Great Doctor. Always he has called them Thekla after the first Thekla but none has ever been quite so mischievous. Perhaps if you were to go to the hospital today, you might see, as one visitor did, a new Thekla curled upon a cushion outside the doctor's study, the white stripe on her back running around her like a ribbon. Or, like another visitor, you might find the Great Doctor sitting on his porch steps beside a small Thekla, singing his favorite German lullabye:

"Lullabye and good night . . ."

Do you suppose that as the doctor sings he thinks of all the Theklas that have come and gone since the first mischievous Thekla put her feet on the fence and begged for orange peels?

On the hospital grounds there are always several baby chimpanzees. There was Fifi, who came to the hospital when she was only a few days old. The Great Doctor and the people at the hospital watched Fifi grow with as much interest as if she had been a human baby. "Fifi has now gotten over her teething," the doctor wrote proudly in a letter to a friend in Europe," and is already able to eat with a spoon."

Fifi came under the special care of Miss Hausknecht, one of the nurses at the hospital. When she fed her, she would tie a bib around her neck, and often the Great Doctor and other doctors would gather around Fifi's chair to watch the performance.

"Now, Fifi," one of them might say, "don't play with your food. Remember your table manners. No splashing!"

Between meals Fifi would follow Miss Hausknecht around like a little child, hanging onto one corner of her apron, tugging at it for attention. And in a playful moment she might, like any small boy or girl, pull at a dangling apronstring to see what would happen.

Another chimpanzee was Fritzi, who is remembered particularly because of his great love for the hospital children. Wherever there was a group of children, there would be Fritzi. He would stand quietly watching for a while and then, whatever they were doing, he would try to join them. He ran with them in the courtyard, he hid with them behind palm trees, he climbed with them, and he tried so hard to play their games. Perhaps Fritzi thought he was one of the children; perhaps no one ever told him anything different.

Romeo and Juliet were two chimpanzees who arrived together and from the very first made it clear that they belonged together. They played and ate together. They shared each other's food. They worried about each other, comforted each other, and sat on tree branches with their arms around each other.

"We shall call them Romeo and Juliet," the

Great Doctor said, finding as always just the right names.

Everyone at the hospital was fond of this loving pair and smiled to watch how well Romeo took care of his Juliet. Then one day Juliet took sick. She began to cough and to run a fever. Poor Romeo! He couldn't do enough for her. He brought her food and tried to coax her to eat it. He sat by her side and did everything he could think of to make her well.

The doctors at the hospital did their best too. They gave her medicine and watched over her carefully, but Juliet was too sick to get well. She died one day and was buried where all the animals who die at the hospital are buried—under a lovely big kapok tree with white flowers on it.

Then the doctors and the nurses tried to comfort Romeo. They found the best things to eat and offered them to him, but he wouldn't eat. Day after day he refused to eat and he refused to be comforted. No matter how all the kind people tried to help him, Romeo was too sad and too lonely without Juliet. He grew so thin that he could live no longer and at last he joined his dear Juliet under the flowering kapok tree.

The hospital monkeys are smaller and noisier than the chimpanzees. From morning to night they clatter across the tin roofs of the hospital buildings. They race up and down palm trees and leap from one fruit tree to another, breaking off bananas and oranges as they go. When a new baby monkey comes to the hospital, he doesn't have to be bibbed and fed like the chimpanzee. There are always plenty of female monkeys who want to adopt the new baby and take care of him.

When Upsi came to the hospital as a new baby monkey, all the older female monkeys crowded around, as they always did, holding out their arms, pushing each other, begging for him. "Me, me!"

they seemed to say. "Give him to me!" They jumped up and down, waving their arms, like children around a schoolteacher when there is only one special job or treat to be given out.

After Upsi was given to a foster mother, he grew up as all monkeys, liking nothing better than to play tricks on someone. The Great Doctor was used to monkeys dropping suddenly out of a tree onto his shoulder, reaching into his pocket, thinking up schemes to steal food. But the Great Doctor will never forget Upsi—not because of any trick he played but because of the time that Upsi, himself, was fooled.

Upsi's special interest was the chicken house. He would figure out all kinds of ways to sneak up to the hen run when no one was looking and steal a freshly laid egg. Feeling very clever, he would dash off with the egg, jump up on a nearby fence, crack the egg and eat it. He loved to do this; he loved the stealing and the eating, and he became bolder and bolder about it.

One day the Great Doctor happened to be walking past the hen run just as Upsi was making off with a stolen egg. What Upsi didn't know was that this time he didn't have a real egg at all. He had a china egg that looks like a real egg but is put in a hen run to encourage the hens to lay more. Somehow when a hen finds this egg, she wants to lay eggs of her own. She can't tell the difference between the make-believe egg and one she has laid. Neither could Upsi. He ran off with the china egg, jumped up on the fence post as usual, and looked over at the doctor as much as to say, "See, I'm so clever I can steal an egg out from under your nose. And I'm so bold I'll eat it in front of you."

While the Great Doctor stood quietly by, Upsi hit the egg against the post to crack it. But the china egg was solid; it didn't crack. Upsi hit it again. Nothing happened.

The Great Doctor put his hands behind his back and smiled. Upsi shook the egg. He banged it and banged it. At last he realized this was no ordinary egg. He gnashed his teeth and hissed in anger, and while the Great Doctor threw back his head and roared with laughter, Upsi threw the china egg to the ground in a tantrum and disappeared into the trees.

For days afterward Upsi sulked. "He is avoiding me," the Great Doctor said. "Naturally, for I saw him being made a fool of."

Josephine came to the hospital when she was
two months old. She was a wild boar who had been
tamed by a native woman.

"She is very gentle," the native woman told the
Great Doctor. "She will follow you around like a
dog and come when you call her."

The Great Doctor smiled and leaned down and
patted Josephine's head. "We shall be good friends
—eh, Josephine?"

Josephine rubbed against the doctor's legs. Then
she sat down to watch while he began to build her
home. He dug very deep into the dirt.

One of the doctor's most trusted Negro helpers, Joseph, was standing near. He smiled. "You can't pen a wild boar," he said.

The doctor dug even deeper. Far down into the earth he sank posts and wire netting.

Still Joseph shook his head. "A wild boar will not remain in a pen," he said. "He digs his way out from under it."

The doctor drove in the last post with a hard blow. "Well," he said, "I should like to see this little wild boar get under this wire netting sunk so deep in the earth."

"You will see," Joseph said. Josephine rubbed against the doctor's legs.

The next morning the doctor stopped at Josephine's pen to say good morning. Josephine was not there. Instead there was a great mound of dirt and a deep hole down one side of the wire netting and up the other. It was clear that Josphine, like Thekla, liked to go and come when she pleased. But when the doctor went to his house at noon, he found her waiting for him. She looked, the doctor reported, as if she wanted to say, "I will remain ever so faithful to you but you must not repeat that trick about the pen."

And, of course, there was no use to try to put her back in the pen. Instead, as the native woman had said, she followed the doctor like a dog and when he called, "Here, Josephine," no matter where she was, she galloped to his side.

For a while she wanted very much to live on the doctor's veranda, but even a tame wild boar isn't as gentle as an antelope nor as easy to live with as a dog. So the doctor had to teach Josephine. "In time," he wrote, "when she had come to understand that she was not permitted to go on the veranda, things became bearable."

One day Josephine disappeared. The Great Doctor called, "Here, Josephine, Josephine," but Josephine didn't come. All day she didn't come. That evening the doctor decided that she must have run off to the jungle and perhaps had met with an accident. He was feeling very sorry when suddenly a native hunter appeared in front of the doctor's house with a gun over his shoulder. Beside him trotted Josephine.

"I was standing in the clearing," the hunter said, "when I saw this wild boar. I was just taking aim, but it came running to me and rubbed against my legs. An extraordinary wild boar!"

So Josephine was back again. By this time she knew enough to stay away from the doctor's veranda but there was one place she could not be taught to keep away from. In spite of everything the doctor could do, every Sunday Josephine was determined to go to church.

Church at the hospital grounds is held out of doors. Doctors and nurses, hospital workers, patients who are well enough and their families, visitors all gather outside on benches and on the ground while the Great Doctor stands in front and conducts the service. Weaver birds sit in the palm trees and chatter; monkeys race across roofs. Dogs and cats and sheep wander among the congregation. This is distracting enough, but wild boars are definitely not invited. Still, there was nothing that Josephine liked better than the Sunday service. As soon as she heard the bell, she ran to church. The doctor tried to tie her at home, but she broke the rope. He made harnesses for her, but she worked her way out of them. He tried to shut her up, but she wouldn't be shut up. No matter how secure he thought he had left her on Sunday morning, somehow she would get away. The Great Doctor might be starting his sermon, thinking that this time, surely, Josephine was safe at home, but always Josephine would appear triumphant, running through the congregation, rubbing herself happily against everyone's legs. The trouble was that almost always she had stopped on the way to church for a little roll in the mud. After a while the doctor decided that if Josephine wanted so much to go to church, there wasn't much that anyone could do about it.

Nor was there much that could be done about Josephine and the boys' dormitory. As soon as it is dark on the Ogowe River, gnats and mosquitoes

come out by the hundreds. People at the hospital don't stay outdoors unless it is necessary, and when they go to sleep, they sleep under mosquito nets.

Gnats, however, are fond of biting animals as well as people, and Josephine had no mosquito net of her own. As soon as the gnats would bother her, she would head for the boys' dormitory. She would wander around until she found the first good mosquito net; then she would crawl up on the bed under the net, pushing in beside whoever was already there. Josephine didn't in the least mind sharing a bed and mosquito net with someone else but the boys in the dormitory felt differently. How many times the Great Doctor has had to apologize for Josephine's behavior and give out presents to angry boys in the dormitory so that they would forgive Josephine her bad manners!

The doctor was always sorry when Josephine bothered other people, but at the same time he couldn't help sympathizing with her and admiring her good sense. After all, if one is bitten by gnats, what more sensible thing is there to do than to look for a mosquito net?

"Ah, Josephine," the doctor once wrote, "how shall I sufficiently praise your wisdom!"

Not all of these friends of the Great Doctor—
Monsieur le Pelican, Leonie, Upsi, Thekla and the
others—have been at the hospital at the same time.
But over all the long years that Dr. Schweitzer has
been in Africa, always there have been animals
round him and near him. Always when he has
walked through the courtyard from his house to
the dining hall there have been dogs to follow him.
Sometimes there has been a favorite like Tchu-
Tchu, a little white dog splashed with yellow
patches. When the other dogs would reach the dining hall, they would stop at the foot of the steps,
but Tchu-Tchu would go on. He would walk up
the steps in front of the doctor and go right into

the dining room, where he was allowed to sit behind the Great Doctor's chair. Before the doctor
sat down at the table himself, he would pick out a
scrap of food and give it to Tchu-Tchu. In the
evening Tchu-Tchu would be invited into the doctor's study for a special, going-to-bed snack.

Always inside the dining hall there has been a
perch for parrots to sit on at their feeding time.
Occasionally after dinner when the doctor has ling-
ered at the table to relax and think by himself, one
of these parrots has flown over to keep him company. Hunched over like an old man, the parrot
has paced thoughtfully back and forth across the
doctor's checkered tablecloth. "If it is a sermon

you are thinking about," he has seemed to say, "perhaps I can help you."

Almost always there has been an antelope under the doctor's porch. Once it was Lucie, then Erica, Jagaguno, and the little dwarf antelope, Pamela, who would never grow to be more than twelve inches tall.

There have been special times, too, when wild things have dropped in from the skies for a short visit at the hospital and then have gone on. No one at the hospital will forget the Christmas when the two storks came. Like two lovely white clouds out of a blue heaven, they dropped quietly down beside the Great Doctor while he was giving his Christmas message at the outdoor church service. They folded their great angel-like wings and, still as two pictures, they stood while the doctor read the story of Bethlehem, while the singing of the carols rose through the palm trees, while the closing prayer was spoken. Then in the evening, almost as if they had planned it before, they rose together and lighted on a roof of the hospital. All that dark Christmas night those two storks stood silhouetted against the African sky, the black jungle behind them. Quietly, like two sentinels of peace, they

watched over the hospital. In the morning they spread their snow-white wings and flew off again into the sunrise.

Then there was another magical evening, although there was no one there that time to see the visitor except the doctor, himself. It was long after the great gong had sounded at half-past nine for lights out, as it does every evening on the hospital grounds. All the little outdoor cooking fires in the village had been put out and the lanterns in the courtyard had been darkened. Over the hospital the Southern Cross glowed—three bright stars and a fainter one, and on this particular night there was a moon. Moonlight sifted down through the palm trees into the courtyard; it turned the banana leaves to silver and the yellow river to a ribbon of running gold. Under the veranda the antelope were asleep and, suspended in their pouch-like nests, the weaver birds were quiet. Work for one day was over.

The Great Doctor went to the piano in his bedroom and, as he often does at this time, he began to play some of his favorite church music. The notes flowed softly into the room, but as the doctor played, all at once he was aware of a faint scuffling noise behind him. A muffled quiet kind of scratch-

ing. Without lifting his hands from the keys, he turned his head to look.

There in a square of moonlight on the floor was a small porcupine dancing in time to the music. He was moving his awkward little body and his short legs back and forth, back and forth as the piano played.

The next morning he was gone.

So part of the true and wonderful story of Dr. Schweitzer is the story of his animals. Surely the animals that have come and stayed with him and even the animals, like the storks and the porcupine, who have come only for a visit, have felt the Great Doctor's reverence for life, his great love for everything that lives, whether large or small. Surely this is why Monsieur le Pelican does not bother to spread his wings for the Big Fight. Surely this is why you will find him today sitting on the Great Doctor's porch roof, the moonlight white on his wings. For, perhaps, he too knows that in all the world there is no country wilder than the country along the long Ogowe River. And in all the world there is no place where there is more love than in this little hospital kingdom where the Great Doctor lives with his animals.